7
10

For Ali, Georgia
and Michael
H.M.
For Joan
P.J.

The publisher and author would like to thank the following for help in checking facts:
Brenda Read and Dr Colin Hardy of Loughborough University, Paul West of the British Cycling Federation,
Gil Carling and Diana Gamble.

First published 1997 by Walker Books Ltd
87 Vauxhall Walk, London SE11 5HJ

2 4 6 8 10 9 7 5 3 1

This book has been typeset in Stone Informal and Birch.

Printed in Italy

British Library Cataloguing in Publication Data
A catalogue record for this book is
available from the British Library.

ISBN 0-7445-3752-5

THE MAGIC STOPWATCH

HEATHER MAISNER

ILLUSTRATED BY **PETER JOYCE**

WALKER BOOKS
AND SUBSIDIARIES
LONDON • BOSTON • SYDNEY

SPORTS CHART

Read the instructions on the next page before you start to play.

	PAGES	SPORT	SPORTING MOMENTS
White	6 and 7	HOME	All games begin and end here!
Red triangle	8 and 9	FOOTBALL	SOCCER · AMERICAN FOOTBALL
Green square	10 and 11	GYMNASTICS	WOMEN'S EVENTS · MEN'S EVENTS
Red circle	12 and 13	BASKET GAMES	NETBALL · BASKETBALL
Blue triangle	14 and 15	STRIKING GAMES	CRICKET · BASEBALL
Yellow square	16 and 17	SNOW SPORTS	UP THE MOUNTAIN · IN THE VALLEY
Yellow circle	18 and 19	FIELD GAMES	RUGBY · HOCKEY
Green triangle	20 and 21	ATHLETICS	TRACK · FIELD
Blue circle	22 and 23	NET GAMES	TENNIS · VOLLEYBALL
Yellow triangle	24 and 25	WATER SPORTS	THE POOL · THE SEA
Blue square	26 and 27	HORSE RIDING	CROSS COUNTRY · IN THE RING
Green circle	28 and 29	CYCLING	MOUNTAIN BIKES · ON THE ROAD

Lost belongings: they are all red

microphone
television
handkerchief
briefcase
tent
lunchbox
bicycle
rucksack
pencil
keys
headphones
computer
radio
camera
umbrella
binoculars
wallet
apple
comb
notebook
deckchair
flask

Lost notes: where did Great Uncle Olympus hear these words?

pivot
striker
silly mid-on
Fosbury Flop
kayak
gridiron
shortstop
love
snap
scrum
pommel horse
bunny hop
boom
T-bar lift
dig
slider
mogul
butterfly
baton
drop-kick
pike dive

HOME · ALL GAMES BEGIN AND END HERE!

Your Great Uncle Olympus, a famous sports commentator, has sent you this letter and a wonderful magic stopwatch. Simply touch it and you will be sent on an exciting journey through the world of sport.

HOW TO BEGIN YOUR JOURNEY

☞ Touch the magic stopwatch, say "**Zoomaswish**" and turn the page. Choose Sporting Moment 1 or Sporting Moment 2 and take part in the action by following The Route through the scene.

☞ When you reach the end of The Route, look for the magic stopwatch hiding somewhere nearby. Be alert! Wherever it goes, the magic stopwatch changes colour, and sometimes it changes shape as well.

Here are three examples:

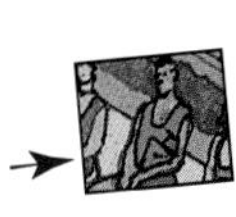

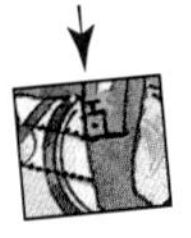

☞ When you have found the magic stopwatch, return to the Sports Chart on page 6. Find the matching stopwatch and turn to the pages numbered beside it. Choose Sporting Moment 1 or 2 and set off again.

☞ Keep going until the magic stopwatch turns WHITE and leads you back Home.

☞ Be sure to look out for ME, too. I'm hiding in three places somewhere in the world of sport. And keep a look-out for my twenty-two **lost belongings** listed on page 6. They are all **red**.

☞ Play with the magic stopwatch as often as you like. Each game will be different – some short, some long.

Have fun and don't get lost!

Great Uncle Olympus

P.S. I've lost some of my **notes**. Can you tell me where the words listed opposite were used?

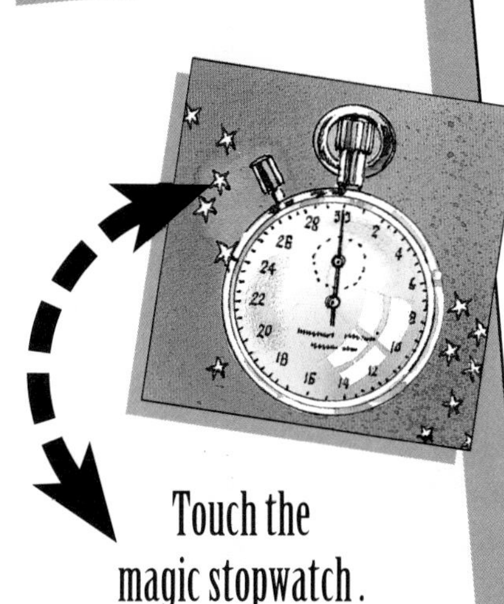

Touch the magic stopwatch. Say "Zoomaswish!"

Missed it!

Oh no!

Tackle!

11

SOCCER

You are at a soccer match with two teams of 11 players. Soccer is short for Association Football. The winning team is the one that manages to score the most goals.

◄-- THE ROUTE --►

☞ Find red player 4 on the sideline. He threw in the ball to restart the game after the stripes kicked it off.

☞ Jump up beside the red centre-half 5. He watched the ball closely and headed it swiftly. Football is one of the few games where you can head the ball.

☞ Run over to striped striker 9, who went for the ball but lost his balance. Then slip past striped defender 4 to number 6, who slid down for a tackle. You need skill and timing to tackle well.

☞ Run to catch up with red left-winger 11. He dribbled the ball down the pitch – keeping it under control, swerving and changing pace. Then he got ready to pass.

☞ Thunder ahead to receive the ball with red striker 10. Make sure you are not offside – there must be at least two opponents between you and the goal when the ball is passed to you. Will you score that dreamed-of goal?

☞ Keep an eye on the goalkeeper waiting to stop you. He will need courage and speed to defend the goal.

☞ Now dash across to the coach holding up card number 11. He wants to substitute a player but has to wait for a break in the game.

☞ SEEK THE MAGIC STOPWATCH

AMERICAN FOOTBALL

You are at a game of American Football. Each team can have up to 45 players, but only 11 are on the pitch at one time. Here the reds are on offense – attacking.

◄-- THE ROUTE --►

☞ Find red centre 50 bending down. He began a play by snapping the ball back – passing it between his legs.

☞ Step back to red quarterback 12, calling "Ready, steady, hut!" He is the team leader, in charge of strategy. He received the snap and passed the ball quickly.

☞ Move across to red half back 42. He caught the ball and is running with it now. Players can pass or run with the ball, but only special kickers can kick it.

☞ Crash! See stars with red guard 80 as he blocks a blue defender, using his whole body. His aim is to protect the half back and create a gap, so that he can run forward and gain ground.

☞ Leap across to blue tackle 56. See that line he's standing on? It represents 5 yards (4.57 m). The pitch is sometimes called a gridiron because it looks like a cooking grill.

☞ Run to the official in a striped shirt bending forward on the right. There are seven officials on the pitch. The chief wears a white cap.

☞ Now run across to join the reds' giant bear mascot. Then kick up a leg with the red cheerleaders. Games last an hour but go on much longer because of stoppages.

☞ SEEK THE MAGIC STOPWATCH

WOMEN'S EVENTS

You are at a gymnastics exhibition watching the women's events, which include asymmetric bars, beam and floor.

◄-- THE ROUTE --►

☞ Find the girl in blue upside down on the beam with legs outstretched. Don't distract her. The beam is only 10 cm wide. It takes years to develop good balance and accuracy.

☞ Step down to the mouse and walk along to two girls with bunches waiting their turn. Tie back your hair and remove all jewellery.

☞ Step up to the girl in pink covered in powder. She wanted to powder her hands with chalk from the bowl behind her, but powdered herself instead. Chalk keeps your hands dry and stops you from slipping.

☞ Swing beside the girl in green on the asymmetric bars. You need strong arms and shoulders. Your timing must be perfect as you move from bar to bar without stopping.

☞ See that girl in a striped tracksuit touching her toes? She is warming up between events. You must stay flexible and supple.

☞ Move on to the large mat where four girls are practising rhythmic gymnastics. Skip gracefully to the music beside the girl in red.

☞ Say hello to the girl balancing a ball and the girl waving a ribbon. Then twirl a hoop beside the girl in yellow. You need skill and elegance for this exciting event.

☞ SEEK THE MAGIC STOPWATCH

MEN'S EVENTS

You are at a gymnastics exhibition watching the men's events, which include vault, pommel horse, rings, high bar and floor.

◄-- THE ROUTE --►

☞ Find the man in red and white making circles on the high bar. He swings around the bar, catching and releasing it with quick, steady hand movements.

☞ Run to greet the master judge in a black suit at the long table. Other judges sit around the hall.

☞ Balance on one hand and move rhythmically along the pommel horse with the man in a green top. Split your legs like scissors and swivel around the handles. Your legs and body must not touch the horse.

☞ Leap across and on to the rings with the man in a black top. Swing slowly upside down with complete control. Go carefully! Hold each position for at least two seconds and do not let the ropes sway.

☞ Hungry? Ask the man eating a banana for a bite. Diet is important. You must keep fit and healthy and make sure that you get enough rest.

☞ Can you see the electronic scoreboard? Difficult jumps and somersaults score high points in competitions, as do perfect landings.

☞ Sprint along the runway to the vault and take off from the blue spring-board with the yellow gymnast. Will you do a double somersault before landing on the mat?

☞ SEEK THE MAGIC STOPWATCH

NETBALL

You are at a netball match, a game for two teams of seven players. Teams score goals by throwing the ball through a ring on a post.

◄-- THE ROUTE --►

☞ Find the goalkeeper, wearing a red bib marked GK. Her job is to stop the green goal shooter behind her from scoring goals. The green team are shooting in the top goal.

☞ Run across to the goal defence, wearing a red bib marked GD. Players wear bibs to show their positions. Each player can only move in certain areas of the court.

☞ Cheer on the red wing attack (WA). She jumped up and caught the ball, then passed it quickly. In netball you must not run with the ball and you cannot hold it for more than three seconds.

☞ Join the green centre (C) trying to dodge free from her opponent. She is the most active player and can go all over the court, apart from the goal areas.

☞ Whoops! The red goal attack (GA) has stepped on someone's foot. In this "no contact" game a player must not touch her opponent when she is trying to get free.

☞ See the umpire running forward to blow her whistle? The game moves very fast. It may need two umpires, a timekeeper and a scorer.

☞ Aim, bend your knees and shoot with the red goal shooter (GS). Concentrate hard and don't be distracted. Only the goal shooter and goal attack (GA) can score goals.

☞ Quickly run all the way back to help the injured player who is lying on the ground. When she came off, a reserve took her place in the game.

☞ SEEK THE MAGIC STOPWATCH

BASKETBALL

You are at a basketball match, a game for two teams of ten players, but only five members of each team are on the court at one time.

◄-- THE ROUTE --►

☞ Find the mice above the big scoreboard and clock. This fast-moving game has many time limits, like a five second rule for releasing the ball when closely marked.

☞ Jump down to the player wearing a blue vest marked 3. Players in each team wear coloured vests to identify them.

☞ Oh dear! Blue 7 has knocked yellow 12 over. In this "no contact" sport, players must not trip, push, hold or charge each other.

☞ Skip ahead to yellow forward 13 who is trying to block his opponent. Players do not have fixed positions. All can pass, shoot and defend anywhere on court.

☞ Run behind the referee wearing white and grey. He controls the game. Can you see the three-point line he has just crossed? Shots taken outside this line are worth three points.

☞ Dribble the ball with the blue guard 10 – keep it below your waist, pushing down with your fingers. You should be able to dribble well with each hand.

☞ Leap across to blue centre 9, waiting to jump up and shoot. Centres are the giants of the game, and are also called posts or pivots. The tallest player ever was 2.45 m.

☞ Stand up and cheer with the supporter in a striped cap. Then warm up with the blue centre 14 waiting at the side to be substituted. In this fast game few players stay on court for the whole match.

☞ SEEK THE MAGIC STOPWATCH

CRICKET

You are at a cricket match. Each team of 11 players takes turns at batting and fielding. Batsmen score runs by running down a narrow pitch between two wooden wickets – stumps.

THE ROUTE

☞ Find the bowler with blond hair. He ran forward, then brought his arm up and over to bowl the ball. The ball must bounce before being hit.

☞ Run ahead to the batsman who has just hit the ball. He kept his eyes on the ball and decided on his stroke, but the ball came so fast he couldn't hit it far enough to make a run.

☞ Squat down behind the wicket with the wicket keeper, wearing gloves and pads. Keep your hands together, your knees bent and your eyes on the ball. Be ready to catch it, if it comes your way.

☞ Now catch the ball with the fielder diving forward. He was in the right place to get the batsman out with a catch. The fielding positions have unusual names and he was standing at "silly mid-on".

☞ Run across and raise one finger high with the umpire in a floppy hat. Umpires use many different hand signals. This one means the batsman is out.

☞ Cheer up the other batsman dragging his bat. He was ready to make a run when his partner hit the ball. The team with the most runs wins. Now his partner is out and he needs to keep his spirits up.

☞ Leap with joy beside the two fielders calling "Howzat" – how was that? – to the umpire. Then run past the seagull to talk to the fielder close to the crowd.

☞ SEEK THE MAGIC STOPWATCH

BASEBALL

You are at a baseball game. Players score runs by hitting the ball and running round a series of bases. The team with the most runs wins.

◄-- THE ROUTE --►

☞ Find the Red Cap pitcher standing on a mound in the centre. He pitched the ball – threw it fast – using a "slider" to confuse the batter. The fastest ball ever was pitched at 162.3 kph.

☞ Join the Blue Shoes batter who has just dropped his bat. He stood at the home-plate to hit the ball, then started to run towards first base.

☞ Go back to the catcher crouching behind the home-plate. Watch out! Some balls come very fast. He wears a head guard, chest plate, leg protectors and a large padded glove.

☞ Step back to the umpire in blue standing behind the catcher. There are four umpires, but he's the one who starts the game.

☞ Run across to the Red Cap fielder, who slipped as he stopped the ball and threw it on. He is the shortstop. Fielders wear one glove to catch the ball but throw it with their ungloved hand.

☞ Reach out for the ball with Red second baseman. Too late! The Blue runner on his knees has made it to second base.

☞ Spread your arms wide with the second base umpire. Umpires use many signals. This one tells the crowd the runner is safe.

☞ Listen! The coach on the left behind third base is calling "run now" to the third base runner. Sprint with him to the home-plate to score a run. Hear the crowd cheer.

☞ Stroll past the batsman holding his bat and waiting his turn. Then join the cat on the roof of the dugout.

☞ SEEK THE MAGIC STOPWATCH

UP THE MOUNTAIN

You are skiing high in the mountains where the air is crystal clear. Skiing began in Scandinavia 4,000 years ago as the best way to travel over snow.

◄-- THE ROUTE --►

☞ Find two girls at the top, on the left wearing pink. They are being gently pulled up on the T-bar lift, which is linked to an overhead cable. Lifts carry you up the mountain so that you can ski down again.

☞ "Schuss" downhill – go very fast – with two men in blue. Use arms for balance as you leap over "moguls" – bumps in the snow. Relax, then bend your knees to cushion the landing. World cup racers can go at 140 kph.

☞ Join the boy on the right using a yellow snowboard – like a surfboard – instead of skis. Stand sideways, bring one foot forward and use your feet to steer. Careful! You need excellent balance.

☞ Race downhill with the girl in red, steering round poles on the slalom course. Control the turns, leaning your weight on to one ski then the next. Don't knock down the poles!

☞ Traverse – go across – the mountain between the two skiers on the track to the man upside down in the snow. He slipped off piste – left the prepared track – perhaps because it was too difficult for him.

☞ Go right and follow two advanced skiers in yellow as they cut a path through fresh untracked snow. Powder snow can be deep and exciting and you need skill to cross it.

☞ Let the wind fill your sails and ski uphill beside the two men holding red and white chutes. Steer from side to side like a water-skier – a dramatic way to climb a mountain.

☞ SEEK THE MAGIC STOPWATCH

IN THE VALLEY

You are in the valley, where young children and beginners learn to ski on nursery slopes. People come here from many different countries. Skiing is an international sport.

◄-- THE ROUTE --►

☞ Find six children and their teachers holding on to a pole for balance and sliding down a slope. This is a way to have fun and gain confidence.

☞ Move back and measure the size of your skis beside the boy in spots. Advanced skiers need skis that reach 10 – 15 cm above the head.

☞ Side-step up the slope with two girls in blue hats. Plant poles firmly and press the uphill edge of each ski into the slope.

☞ Want to ramble through frozen forests? Follow cross-country skiers striding beside trees on the right, wearing long narrow skis.

☞ Tired? Speed back on a yellow snowmobile – a sled with a motor. Then stop and follow four children skiing down the slope without poles. Keep your skis in the snowplough position – a "V" – for gliding, turning and stopping.

☞ Help the man sitting in the snow. He is trying to stand up by pushing on his poles, but his feet are sliding away from him. Tell him to keep his skis together across the slope or he will never get up.

☞ Climb up to help the girl in a yellow top carrying skis on one shoulder. Tell her to be careful how she turns. Whoops! Too late!

☞ Ski round giant snowmen with children from kindergarten – nursery school. Keep slow and steady. Control your speed with skis in the snowplough position, and don't crash into your friends.

☞ SEEK THE MAGIC STOPWATCH

RUGBY

You are at a game of rugby union with two teams of 15 players. This is a scrum – a way to start up the game again after a foul.

◄-- THE ROUTE --►

☞ Find the referee in black. He checked that all the players were in the right place before the scrum began. Then the teams locked arms and pushed forward to gain the ball.

☞ Bend forward with the red scrum-half with ginger hair. He held the ball in both hands and put it straight into the middle of the tunnel between the two teams.

☞ Can you see the back of striped hooker 2? His team pushed forward so well that he got the ball and hooked it backwards with his foot.

☞ Squeeze arms and grip tight with the striped second row. It's hot and steamy in here. Mind the mud! Now help kick the ball back to striped number 8 at the rear of the scrum.

☞ Leap across to the striped scrum-half 9 with blond hair. He swept up the ball and threw it. In rugby you can throw, kick and carry the ball, but you cannot throw it forwards.

☞ Charge across to the striped fly-half 10. Watch as he drops the ball to the ground for a drop-kick – a powerful kick on the bounce.

☞ Now follow the ball as it zooms towards the goal. Will it go over the cross bar and score three points? The team with the most points wins.

☞ SEEK THE MAGIC STOPWATCH

HOCKEY

You're at a hockey match with 11 players on each side, all using hooked sticks. This is a penalty corner – a way to restart play after a stoppage.

◄-- THE ROUTE --►

☞ Find yellow player 9. She stood astride the back line to take the penalty and hit the ball hard with the flat side of her stick, the only side you can use.

☞ Run forward to yellow 3. She waited outside the shooting circle with the rest of the yellow attackers. Then she stopped the ball with her stick and passed it quickly.

☞ Dash forward to blue 7. She lined up in defence, then tried to reach the ball before it got to yellow 3. This time she was too late. You must act quickly under pressure.

☞ Leap across to yellow 6. She ran into the circle, received the pass and whacked it hard at the goal with speed and accuracy. Did you hear the ball crack against the stick?

☞ Quickly! Slide down with the goalkeeper, the only player who can stop the ball with her body. Move on to blue 2, ready to clear the ball if the goalkeeper needs help.

☞ Whoops! Something is flying out of the mouth of blue 4. It's her gum shield. Players must protect themselves well. The ball can travel at over 140 kph.

☞ Now join the reserve player near the crowd bouncing a ball on her stick. You need good co-ordination of hand, ball and eye.

☞ SEEK THE MAGIC STOPWATCH

TRACK

You are at a sports stadium, where many different races take place on the track. It has eight lanes and is 400 m all the way round.

◄-- THE ROUTE --►

☞ Find two runners both wearing red, passing a baton at speed. They are practising for the relay race, when four sprinters work as a team.

☞ Jog on to blue sprinter 7 crouching down to tighten the spikes on his shoes with a spanner. Spikes grip the track and stop you sliding on wet days.

☞ See the official with his arm raised, holding a pistol? He fired a shot to start the women's 100 m hurdles race. There can be over 100 officials at the stadium.

☞ Step across to the starting blocks in the numbered lanes. The hurdlers lined up here, leaning forward with their feet against the blocks. When the shot was fired, they sped away.

☞ Help the hurdler in lane 3. She leapt up, hit the hurdles and lost her rhythm. Hurdlers need to "run tall"– keeping good speed and rhythm as they go over and between the barriers.

☞ Now join the hurdler in lane 4. See her leap hard and low across the hurdle before bringing her back leg through swiftly.

☞ Sprint ahead and join the judge in a red blazer at the finishing line. Electronic equipment will photo the finish, but timekeepers must pass exams for accuracy.

☞ Follow the track all the way round and look up at the large TV screen above. See the lead hurdler pull one arm back and punch the air with the other hand as she jumps over the hurdle.

☞ SEEK THE MAGIC STOPWATCH

FIELD

You are at a stadium for the field events. Athletes compete to jump or throw the highest and the furthest.

◄-- THE ROUTE --►

☞ Find the athlete on a stretcher whose leg has been taped by a doctor. She has strained a muscle. You need at least 20 minutes warming up to raise your body temperature and loosen your joints.

☞ Join the long jumper flying across the sand. She ran swiftly to build up speed, then continued to stride through the air after take-off. The longest jump ever was 8.95 m.

☞ Tired and breathless? Climb on the podium and join in the prize-giving ceremony. Raise arms with the winner and smile at the crowd.

☞ Now spring upside down in the air beside the pole-vaulter. Release the pole and land on the red foam bed. In ancient times people used poles like this to cross canals without a bridge.

☞ See the athlete practising with a javelin? Later she will run forward, pulling the javelin up and over her shoulder to hurl it into the sky. Go carefully. It has a point at both ends.

☞ Leap up to do the "Fosbury Flop" beside the high jumper in blue and white. He ran, took off from one foot and jumped up head-first. Soon he will flop down and land on his back on the yellow safety mat.

☞ Do you dare join the discus thrower inside the wire cage, who is still spinning from getting up speed? His balance and timing were perfect. When he released the discus, it zoomed through the air.

☞ Run forward to the official, about to measure the throw. Will it beat the world record of 74.08 m?

☞ SEEK THE MAGIC STOPWATCH

TENNIS

You are at a doubles tennis match. Players score points by hitting a ball over a net and making it difficult to return.

◄-- THE ROUTE --►

☞ Find the player with a blue cap running forward. He served to start the game. Can you see the ball in his pocket? Servers sometimes need a second ball.

☞ Leap across to his partner in a white skirt. She moved close to the net and volleyed the ball – hit it without waiting for it to bounce.

☞ Climb up beside the umpire calling out the score. You can get a good view from up here. There are officials at the back and side of the court, and a net-cord judge at the net. But the umpire's word is final.

☞ Oh dear! Two players have crashed into each other. The man was holding his racket ready for a backhand stroke, with the back of his racket facing the ball.

☞ Stop his partner from toppling over. She was holding her racket ready for a forehand stroke and he should have guessed what she would do. Doubles needs good team work.

☞ See the bird landing between white lines down the side of the court? The extra space between these lines is needed for a doubles match.

☞ Look up at the scoreboard. The score is forty-love. "Love" comes from the French word for egg – *l'oeuf* – the shape of zero.

☞ SEEK THE MAGIC STOPWATCH

VOLLEYBALL

You are at a volleyball game on the beach. Two teams of six hit a ball over the net, mostly using their hands or arms.

◄-- THE ROUTE --►

☞ Find the server in spotty shorts. He tossed the ball, struck it with one hand and sent it spinning over the net. When a team wins the serve, players move round clockwise.

☞ Run under the net to the player in a green cap. He received the serve with a dig – bent his knees, locked his arms, gritted his teeth and hit the ball when it was below his waist.

☞ Leap up with the player all in green who pushed the ball away quickly. Teams can hit the ball up to three times without knocking it over the net. But no player can hit the ball twice in a row.

☞ Race across to the player in the yellow swimsuit. She smashed the ball across the net so hard that she hopes nobody will return it.

☞ Jump up with the two players forming a wall above the net to block the smash. Look frightening. You want to put the other team off.

☞ Help the player who has skidded, then run back for extra training with the boy lifting weights. You need good muscles, strong arms, speed and flexibility.

☞ Feeling tired? Join the long line of spectators. Say hello to the girl with the ice-cream, then flop down beside the man on a striped towel.

☞ SEEK THE MAGIC STOPWATCH

THE POOL

You are at the pool for a swimming competition, where swimmers need hard work and dedication. This is a practice session.

◄-- THE ROUTE --►

☞ Find lane 1 and join the swimmer in red about to dive in. You need a shallow dive for a racing start.

☞ Swim across to lane 2 and join the swimmer doing back crawl. Move your arms like a windmill and kick your legs up and down, resting your head on the water.

☞ Move into lane 3 and do the breaststroke. Circle your arms and kick your legs in and out like a frog. Stretch, pull and breathe, kick and glide.

☞ Now turn and join the swimmer doing butterfly stroke in lane 4. Pull your arms up and over the water and kick your legs together like a dolphin's tail.

☞ Say hello to the three timekeepers in grey on the right. In a race there can also be stroke judges, turn judges, place judges and a referee.

☞ Look up at the line of colourful marker flags. They let backstrokers know when they are 5 m from the end of the pool.

☞ Whoops, the swimmer in lane 5 is moving out of lane. Tell her to be careful. In a race she would be disqualified if she obstructed someone.

☞ Race ahead with the swimmer in lane 6 doing front crawl, the fastest stroke of all. Pull strongly with your arms. The fastest time ever swum for 100 m was 46.74 seconds.

☞ Now go to the small pool, climb up the steps and do a spectacular pike dive from the platform. Bend your body at the hips and keep your legs together and your toes pointed. Be as graceful as a gymnast.

☞ SEEK THE MAGIC STOPWATCH

THE SEA

You are by the sea for a day of swimming and boating. Feel the spray on your face. You need lots of skill to sail the seas.

◄-- THE ROUTE --►

☞ Find two people in blue caps, demonstrating life-saving techniques. The rescued swimmer is on her side in the recovery position with one leg bent to help avoid choking.

☞ Help the young girl put on her yellow life jacket. It keeps her afloat in the water. Life jackets must be worn by everyone in a boat.

☞ Scan the waves with three lifeguards in blue shorts. They are expert swimmers, ready to take action and rescue anyone in trouble.

☞ See the man dressed in a wetsuit wading into the water with breathing equipment strapped to his back? He is going scuba-diving to study life under the waves.

☞ Now ride the surf with windsurfer 79. Hold on to the boom – the pole which works the sail. You need good control and excellent balance.

☞ Move across to paddle in the kayak – covered canoe. Canoes were used as transport over 6,000 years ago.

☞ Say hello to the dog riding in a dinghy – small boat. Then jet-ski through the waves with two people in yellow. You need the skills of a waterskier and a motor cyclist.

☞ Jump into sailing boat number 11 and sail out to the tall ship with three masts and lots of sails. Sailing means using the wind to move through the water. When there's no wind you can't move.

☞ Hear that loud noise? It's the motorboat with a water-skier in tow. See him swerve through the water but keep out of his way.

☞ SEEK THE MAGIC STOPWATCH

CROSS COUNTRY

You are at the Horse Trials for the cross-country course, which covers over 4 km and has at least 20 fixed obstacles. You and your horse must be bold and fast.

◄-- THE ROUTE --►

☞ Find the white tent, where a vet is examining a horse. All horses must be fit before events. If your horse stumbles, starts to breathe hard or loses rhythm, stop at once.

☞ Start the race and jump over the logs with the brown horse. Make sure your horse is paying attention, then go faster and find your rhythm.

☞ Go at a canter – a gentle, steady ride – towards the next jump. This wide obstacle is called the chair.

☞ Now turn and approach the hayrack fence. Move as one with your horse and jump confidently but carefully.

☞ See those two fences on the left? This is the bounce – a difficult combination jump. You must clear each fence without taking a stride between them.

☞ Oh dear, the grey horse has refused the next jump – the drainpipes. Talk to him so that he will try again. If he refuses three times, he will be eliminated.

☞ Turn and ride towards the solid tree trunk, where two judges are standing. Judges wait by each fence to mark the riders and check that the rules are followed.

☞ Follow the rider in blue over the water jump. Be firm or your horse may be frightened and refuse. Some horses don't like water. Now turn and wave to the family having a picnic as they watch the competition.

☞ SEEK THE MAGIC STOPWATCH

IN THE RING

You are at the show-jumping ring during the Horse Trials, which were originally a test for military horses. The aim is to jump the course swiftly and without any faults.

◄-- THE ROUTE --►

☞ Find the red flag where a bird is sitting. You are at the start. Ride on and prepare your horse to jump the first fence, an upright with red and white bars.

☞ Whoops! The rider ahead has knocked the top bar from the second fence and a steward is putting it back. The rider was awarded a five point penalty. The one with fewest points wins.

☞ Gather rhythm, control your horse and join the rider leaping over the triple bar. This spread fence has a high rail at the back, so your horse must stretch high and wide.

☞ Turn left and adjust your stride for the next jump – the wall. Take your time then approach and jump with perfect balance.

☞ Oh dear! Your horse has refused the water jump for the third time! This means he has been eliminated from the competition.

☞ Join the girl on a light grey horse watching the show. Then move on to the girl washing down her horse. Borrow a sponge and scraper to help her.

☞ Urge the dappled horse into his horse-box, then run after the horse which has bolted. Perhaps he had a fright. It is important to keep your horse calm.

☞ Now move towards the man with a top hat on a brown horse in the far ring. He is doing the Dressage Test. This test aims to show perfect harmony between horse and rider. Join the people watching him.

☞ SEEK THE MAGIC STOPWATCH

MOUNTAIN BIKES

You are at a cross-country race. Look out for slippery roots and mud. Be prepared for bumps and jumps.

◄-- THE ROUTE --►

☞ Find the blue cyclist on the left doing a bunny hop over a log. He leans back to lift the front wheel before putting his weight forward to lift the back wheel – the best way to cross obstacles without dismounting.

☞ Climb uphill beside the red cyclist, but don't follow the purple rider off route and into the woods. You could be disqualified if you leave the set route.

☞ Shout "track" as a warning as you overtake the green cyclist. Then race on to the boy who has fallen, damaging his bike. All riders must carry their own tool kits.

☞ Follow the track round and race downhill with three cyclists. Push hard on the handlebars, lifting yourself up out of the saddle. Let the bike float along, absorbing shocks. Hang on tight!

☞ Cross the stream and tell the pink rider she's going the wrong way. Follow the path and do a wheelie beside the cyclist in green, balancing on your rear wheel as you approach the rocks.

☞ Do a double wheelie bunny hop beside the the rabbit, lifting both wheels off the ground at once to cross the ditch.

☞ Cycle through the mud then dismount and raise your bike beside number 18. He is doing a running jump over fallen branches.

☞ SEEK THE MAGIC STOPWATCH

ON THE ROAD

You are nearing the end of a road race. Cyclists start together and follow a set course. They work in teams using tactics to help each other and confuse opponents.

◄-- THE ROUTE --►

☞ Find the black van with bikes on the roof. It is called a sag wagon and is used for picking up riders who have dropped out.

☞ Move on to the last cyclist in red, struggling to keep up. Road racing needs speed, skill, stamina, strong legs and good tactics.

☞ Join the main bunch and ride close behind another cyclist to conserve energy and effort. This is called slipstreaming.

☞ Pedal hard to reach the rider in blue taking his turn at the front of the bunch. He works hard to create a path through the air stream.

☞ Oh no! The cyclist in green has a puncture. He must wait for the service car. It carries spare wheels.

☞ Ride on and say hello to the two motor cyclists ahead. They keep the roads clear of vehicles.

☞ Overtake the yellow and blue service cars with bikes on their roofs. Say hello to two marshalls in grey at the side of the road. They check that you obey the rules of the road.

☞ Glance at the commissaire – main judge – in the black car, then sprint ahead to be the first cyclist across the finishing line. Now wave to your mother in a yellow hat among the crowd.

☞ SEEK THE MAGIC STOPWATCH